Sometimes all it
takes is a word!

Steph
2017

Written by	**Stephen Kok**
Artwork by	**P.R. Dedelis**
Colours by	**Peyton Freeman**

For Judy and Eri

Word Smith

Created and written by Stephen Kok
Illustrated by P.R. Dedelis
Coloured by Peyton Freeman

Sigmate Studio
www.sigmatestudio.com

First Edition: Oct 2017

ISBN: 978-0-9942899-4-0

10 9 8 7 6 5 4 3 2 1

Word Smith is supported by Creative Partnerships Australia.
Printed in Australia by Comic Books on Demand.

creative partnerships australia

www.comicbooksondemand.com.au

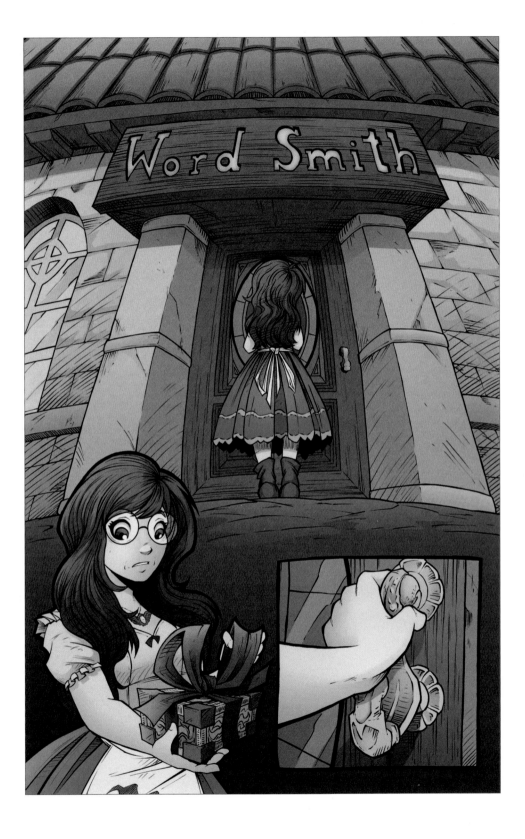

HMMM. HAVEN'T SEEN HIM.

I HAVE TO FIND THIS MAN. HE IS DANGEROUS, AND I HAVE TO STOP HIM FROM HARMING ANYONE ELSE.

OH MY.

HAVE YOU BEEN UP AND DOWN THIS AIRSHIP DOCK?

I HAVE BEEN UP AND DOWN THE DOCK.

I'VE BEEN TOLD HE WILL BE IN THIS TOWN FOR SUPPLIES BUT I COULD NOT FIND HIM.

YOU'VE CHECKED THE OTHER DOCK AS WELL?

THERE'S ANOTHER DOCK?

IT IS ON THE OTHER SIDE OF TOWN.

THANK YOU! MAYBE I'LL FINALLY BE ABLE TO CATCH HIM.

IS *WAR* COMING?

READ ALL ABOUT IT!

WAR?

WAR?

CAN I TRY STEERING?

SHE'S ALL YOURS.

HAND TIGHT ON WHEEL.

WE ARE GETTING CLOSE. LOWER LEVER.

THIS WILL LOWER THE PRESSURE.

LIKE THIS?

GOOD. GOOD.

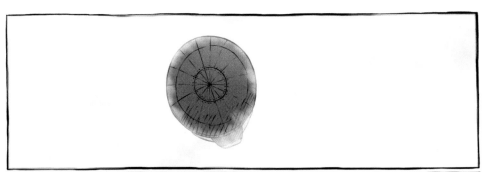

THIS VIEW IS
INCREDIBLE!

GEORGE! WAIT!

I KNOW YOU. YOU'RE THE WORD SMITH. WHAT ARE YOU DOING HERE?

I CAUSED ALL OF THIS. I'M HERE TO ASK YOU TO PLEASE GO HOME TO BONNIE.

I KNOW THE PAIN I'VE CAUSED BONNIE BUT I WOULD END UP HURTING HER MORE IF I STAYED.

YOU HAVE . .

I HAVE TO FIX . .

NO. YOU DON'T UNDERSTAND. I DO REALLY LOVE BONNIE BUT EVERY DAY IN THE BAKERY WAS TAKING AWAY A PART OF MY SOUL.

YOU DID EVERYTHING YOU COULD. IT'S NOT YOUR FAULT.

DA. HE WAS A GOOD FRIEND. A LONG TIME AGO.

YOU HAVE FOUND GEORGE. DO WHAT YOU NEED AND I WILL TAKE YOU HOME.

PLEASE OPEN IT.

The End

CHARACTER DESIGN & STORYBOARDS

CHARACTER DESIGN

Victoria and Sparky

When initially designing Victoria, I always imagined her looking like a mechanic. The other character elements were easy with her steampunk goggles and her trademark scarf.

I knew Victoria needed a companion and I did consider quite a few options including a hedgehog and a red panda. (Don't worry I have saved the red panda to be introduced in the next story arc!) However, once I settled on having some fantasy elements in the world of Word Smith, it was easy to settle on a baby dragon called Sparky.

Dimitri and Celia

Dimitri is a sky captain with a past. His design was based on a muscular Russian who may look very imposing but had a kind heart. Writing the dialogue for Dimitri was fun and it was easy to give him a distinctive voice in Word Smith.

Celia is tomboyish and her clothes are hand me downs with a jacket and scarf that's too big for her. Despite her hard upbringing, I wanted her to still have look of innocence and wonder.

STORYBOARD 1

It's incredible to see the amount of work that P.R. Dedelis puts into a page. This is the first time the reader gets to see Victoria and Sparky in the graphic novel.

The penciled page sharpens all the details and gets the page ready to be inked. I do love how Sparky has stolen Victoria's hammer after she ate the last cake!

STORYBOARD 2

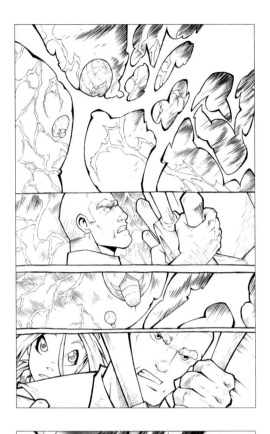

This is one of my favourite pages in Word Smith as our heroes flew through a lightning storm. The inked page was fantastic with the artist P.R. Dedelis capturing so much detail.

It's the colours that take it to the next level, with the lightning flashes casting light and shadows on Victoria's and Dimitri's faces.

TABBY

Tabby's idyllic world is changed when a new family of cats move into the neighbourhood. To make things more complicated, Tabby Junior falls in love with a cat from the other family!

ISBN 9780994289902   ISBN 9780994289919

5 SECONDS

Jake's life changes when he discovers he can see what happens 5 seconds into the future. With his best friend Ellie, the two of them decide to test out exactly what Jake can do. Unfortunately, others also find out about Jake's power and they seek to exploit his unique time-bending skill!

All graphic novels are currently available from all good bookstores in Australia and New Zealand OR online retailer.

www.sigmatestudio.com

www.facebook.com/sigmatestudio

@sigmatestudio

ISBN 9780994289926

Illustrated by Eric Gravel